Hi, kids! You know me, Eleanor the Elephant! My friends and I are taking a tour around our town! Come along with us, and be sure to bring your pencil! First stop, the Fire Station!

See these stickers? Every time you learn something new, you get a star sticker. When you finish each section, you'll get a special train sticker to put on your Certificate of Completion at the end of the book.

One more thing! When you see this picture of me, it means I am there to give you a little help. Just look for **Eleanor's Tips**.

## Eleanor's Tips

**Rhyming words** have endings that sound the same. C**at** and h**at** rhyme.

Here we are at the fire station!

**Help the fire fighters slide down the pole! Say each picture name out loud. Draw a line between the pictures that rhyme.**

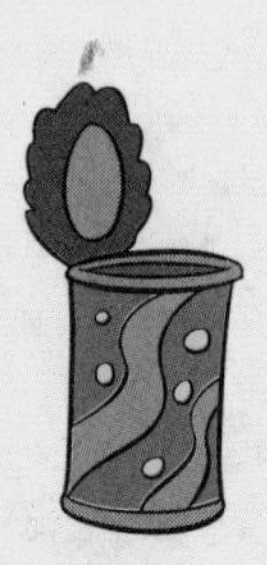

Now help the climb on board.

**Look at the pictures at the bottom of the page and say each picture name out loud. Then match the rhyming pictures by drawing lines to connect them.**

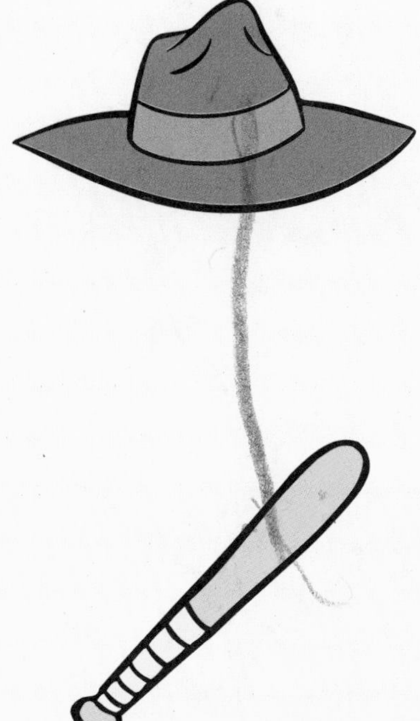

**Good job! Place your star sticker here.
Now jump ahead to the next page.**

Spot is in a hurry to help put out a fire!

**Help him get there. Put an X on each picture whose name rhymes with**  **.**

The firehouse is a mess! Help us clean up!

**Circle the pictures that rhyme with [bear] in blue.**

**Circle the picture that rhymes with [stop] in red.**

**Circle the pictures that rhyme with [boat] in yellow.**

**Circle the pictures that rhyme with [bat] in green.**

Level 2

Shhh! Everyone is sleeping. Help us find our things in the dark.

**Say the name of each object out loud. Then draw lines between the words that rhyme.**

Level 2

Let's take a walk. Help us find these things around town.

**Circle:**

**something that rhymes with** (star)
**something that rhymes with** (bee)
**something that rhymes with** (door)

**Great job! Place your star sticker here.**
**Now jump ahead to the next page.**

## Eleanor's Tips

To make rhyming words, change the beginning sound. To change cat to bat, change **c** to **b**.

**c**at **b**at

Help us figure out what each store sells. Look at the picture in each window.

**Follow the lines from the blanks to the letters. Then copy the letters onto the lines.**

__AN __AN __AT __AT

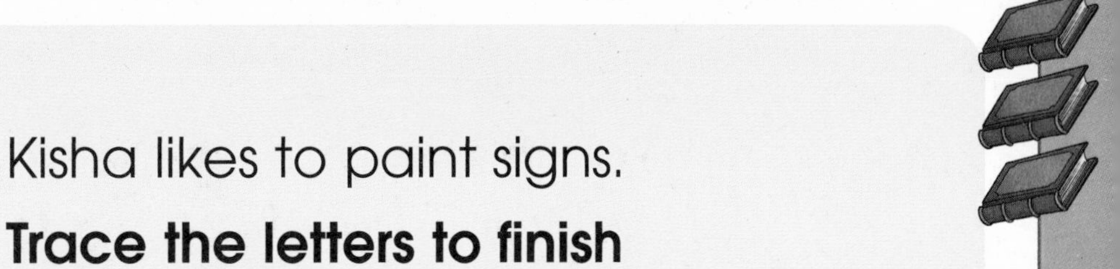

Kisha likes to paint signs.

**Trace the letters to finish each word.**

Level 3

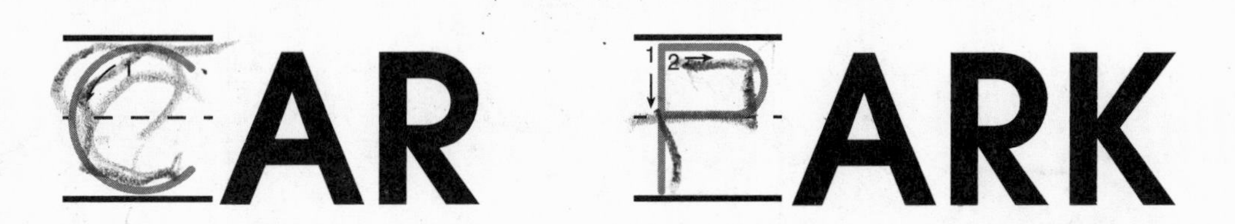

**Now, can you name another word that rhymes with PARK and BARK?**

**Great job! Place your star sticker here.**
**Now jump ahead to see what you've learned.**

You can play this memory game by yourself or with a friend! You'll need a deck of playing cards.

**Cover each rectangle with a playing card. Then pick up the cards on any two spaces. Say the two picture names out loud.**

If they rhyme, you have a match and you can keep the cards! If they do not rhyme, put back the cards and try again. Keep going until you have collected all the cards.

Excellent! Place a train sticker on your Certificate of Completion. Now jump ahead for more fun.

Someone is hiding something from me! It rhymes with GO ! Help me find it!

**Circle what I am missing.**

Someone is hiding something from Pierre.
It rhymes with 🦴.

**Help him find it. Draw a circle around it.**

Level 1

**Great job! Place your star sticker here.**
**Now jump ahead to the next page.**

Help the firefighters do their job by answering this riddle.

She's Casey's friend!
She says "Meow."
She rhymes with [bat].
Can you find her now?

**Circle the answer.**

Help us find the cat's owner by answering this riddle.

He is not a boy.
This cat is his.
He rhymes with .
Can you guess who he is?

**Circle the answer.**

Help us find our way around town by answering this riddle.

If you're lost or if you're found,
It shows you how to get around!
It rhymes with [cap].
It is a _____!

**Circle the answer.**

Help us with our picnic by answering this riddle.

It rhymes with ◎.
It's not easy to catch.
It knows how to swim.
It's a great big _____!

**Circle the answers.**

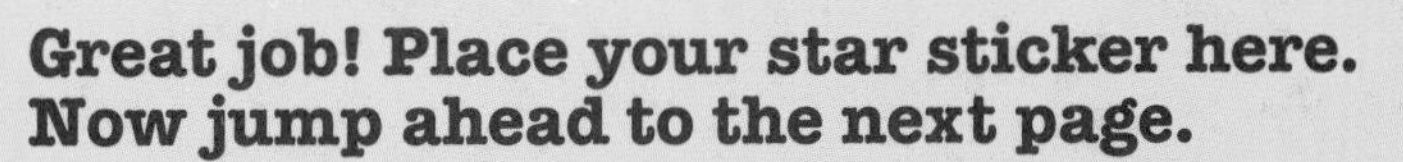

**Great job! Place your star sticker here.**
**Now jump ahead to the next page.**

# Eleanor's Tips

Here's how you write the letters **B** and **D**. Just follow the arrows.

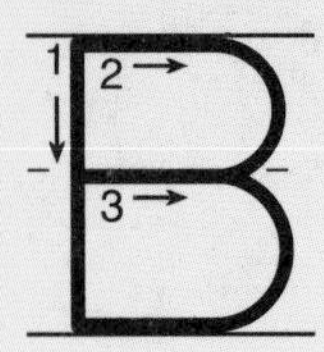


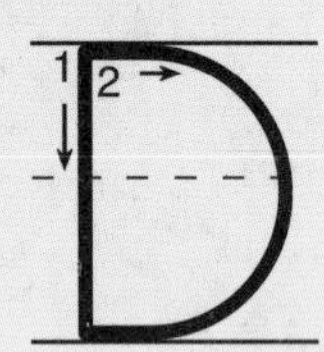


Quick! Help us! Answer this riddle!

I say "Buzz."
I rhyme with .
Who am I?
I am a __ee!

**Trace the first letter of the word to solve the riddle.**

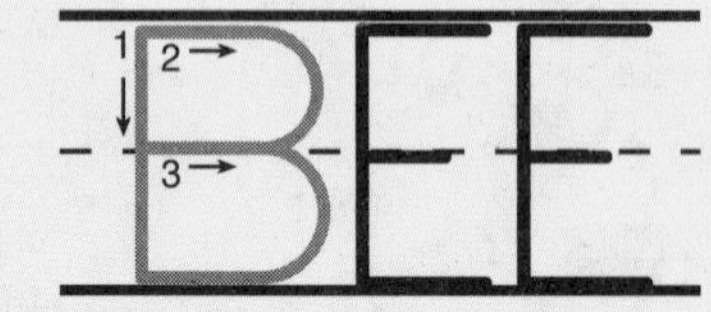

Help steer the way by answering this riddle.

I say "Quack."
I rhyme with .
I float all day.
I am a __uck.

**Trace the first letter of the word to solve the riddle.**
**Then circle the ducklings hiding along the shore.**

**Excellent job! Place your star sticker here.**
**Now jump ahead to see what you've learned.**

There are letters all over this island! You can play by yourself or with a partner.

**Look at the letters on Letter Island. Use them to make a word on each space on the board.**

Some have more than one answer. When you get to the finish line, go back and say each word out loud! There are some clues in the water.

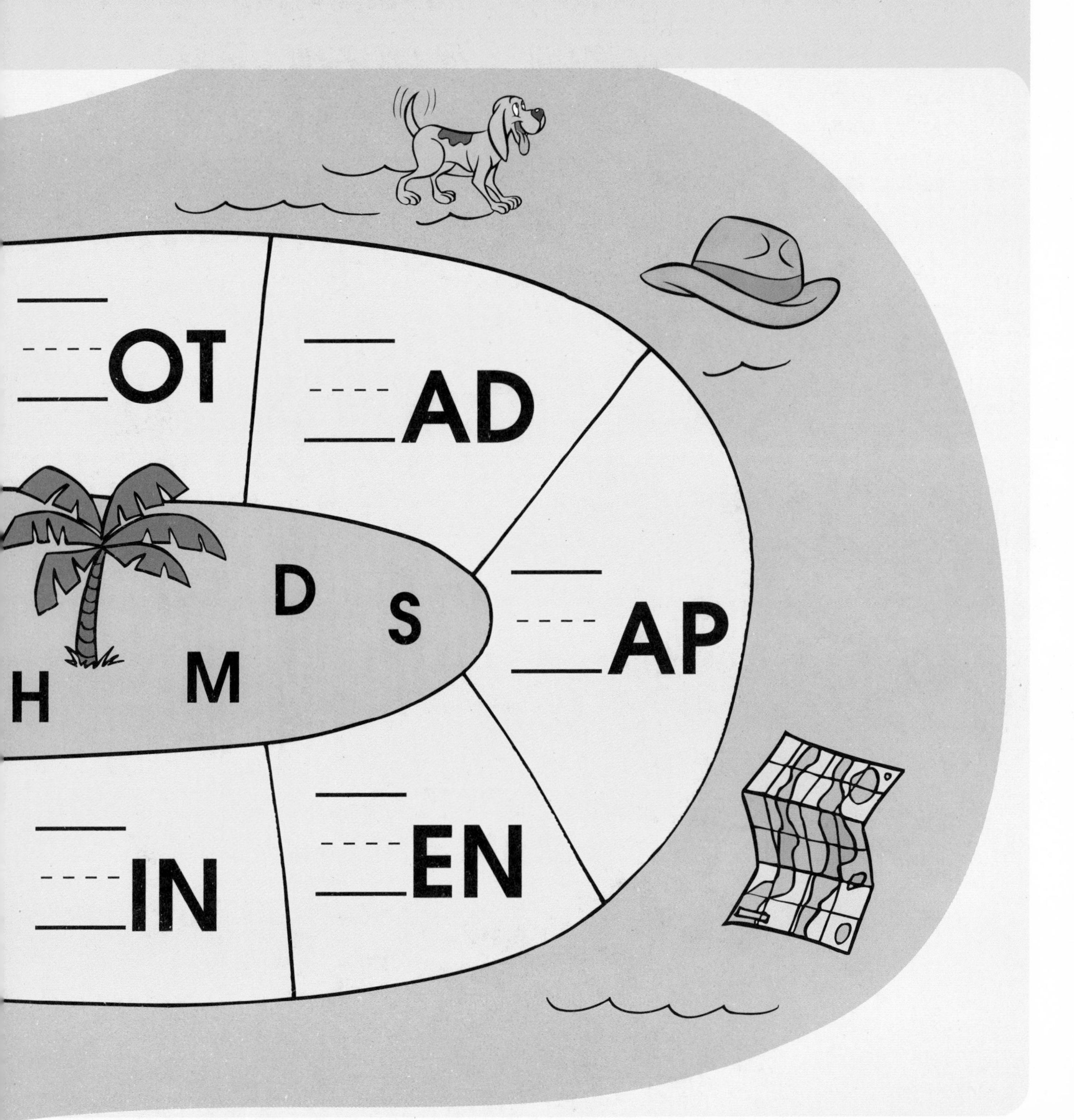

## Eleanor's Tips

A **poem** is a special way of using words. Sometimes words in poems rhyme.

Our next stop is the library. It's story hour!

**Read this rhyme. Then color the pictures on the big book.**

Jack and Jill went up the hill to fetch a pail of water. Jack fell down and broke his crown, and Jill came tumbling after.

Let's read another story! **Read this rhyme.**
**Then color the pictures on the big book.**

There was an [old woman] who lived in a [shoe].
She had so many children she didn't know what to do.
She gave them some broth without any [bread],
and sang to them sweetly and sent them to [bed].

Good job! Place your star sticker here.
Now jump ahead to the next page.

Can you find the pictures on our farm?

**Read this rhyme. In the picture below, circle the pictures that match the ones in the rhyme.**

Little  blue, come blow your .
The 's in the meadow, the 's in the .
Where is the  who looks after the ?
He's under the , fast asleep.

**Read this rhyme. Then color in the fish in order.**

1, 2, 3, 4, 5,
Once I caught a fish alive.
6, 7, 8, 9, 10,
Then I let it go again.

**Read this rhyme.**

Little Bo Peep has lost her ,
And doesn't know where to find them.
Leave them alone and they'll come home,
Wagging their tails behind them.

**Now circle the**  **.**

**Read this rhyme.**

Humpty Dumpty sat on a [wall].
Humpty Dumpty had a great [fall].
All the King's [horses] and
All the King's men
Couldn't put Humpty together again.

**Can you find the King's [horses]? Circle them.**

**Great job! Place your star sticker here.**
**Now jump ahead to the next page.**

# Eleanor's Tips

**M** says "mmmmmm" and **E** says "eeeeee." Put them together and you've got **ME**! Here's how you write the letter M. Just follow the arrows.

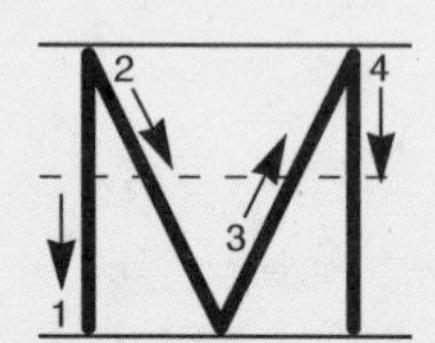


Now we're hungry! The bakery is right around the corner—and I have the perfect rhyme! Mmmmm!

Pat-a-cake, pat-a-cake,
Baker's man,
Bake me a cake
As fast as you can.
Pat it, and prick it,
And mark it with a **B**,
And put it in the oven
For Baby and ___e!

**Write the first letter of the word** ME **on the line below!**

Oh, how I wish I had a spoon. That reminds me of a riddle! It goes like this:

Hey diddle diddle, the cat and the fiddle,
The cow jumped over the moon.
The little dog laughed to see such fun,
And the dish ran away with the _poon.

**Trace the first letter of the word spoon.**

**Excellent! Place your star sticker here.**
**Now jump ahead to see what you've learned.**

Look, the fish need our letters!

**Write M, C, P, or S on the lines to make complete words. Some letters work on more than one fish!**

Way to go! Put your last train sticker on your Certificate of Completion. You did it!

# Answer Key

| | |
|---|---|
| PAGE 2 | draw lines to connect map/cap, fan/can, hat/bat |
| PAGE 3 | draw lines to connect coat/boat, hat/bat, truck/duck |
| PAGE 4 | draw an X on hat, bat, bat |
| PAGE 5 | circle pears blue, circle mop red, circle coats yellow, circle hats green |
| PAGE 6 | draw lines to connect bug/mug, fan/can, hat/cat |
| PAGE 7 | circle car, tree, store |
| PAGE 8 | write F, C, B, H |
| PAGE 9 | trace C, P, B; answers will vary |
| PAGES 10–11 | match bat/hat, car/jar, pan/can, mop/top, cap/map, bug/mug |
| PAGE 12 | circle bow |
| PAGE 13 | circle cone |
| PAGE 14 | circle cat |
| PAGE 15 | circle man |
| PAGE 16 | circle map |
| PAGE 17 | circle the fish |
| PAGE 18 | trace B |
| PAGE 19 | trace D |
| PAGES 20–21 | write bat, hat, fat, mat, *or* sat; ban, fan, man, *or* tan; dot, hot, *or* tot; bad, dad, fad, had, mad, *or* sad; map *or* tap; den, hen, men, *or* ten; bin, din, fin, sin, *or* tin; big, dig, *or* fig; bog, dog, fog, *or* hog; bop, hop, mop, *or* top |
| PAGE 22 | color pictures on book |
| PAGE 23 | color pictures on book |
| PAGE 24 | circle boy, horn, sheep, cow, corn, haystack |
| PAGE 25 | color fish from 1 to 10 |
| PAGE 26 | circle three sheep |
| PAGE 27 | circle horses |
| PAGE 28 | write M |
| PAGE 29 | trace S |
| PAGES 30–31 | MAD, PAD, *or* SAD; MAN, CAN, *or* PAN; MAP, CAP, *or* SAP; COT *or* POT; MAT, CAT, PAT, *or* SAT; MAIL, PAIL, *or* SAIL |

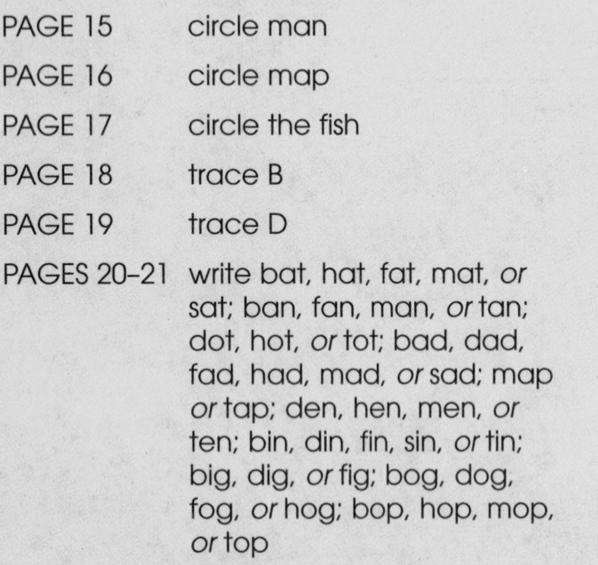